Maths

The 11+ Practice Book

with Assessment Tests

Ages
8-9

Practise • Prepare • Pass

Everything your child needs for 11+ success

How to use this Practice Book

This book is divided into two parts — themed question practice and assessment tests.
There are answers and detailed explanations in the pull-out section at the end of the book.

Themed question practice

- Each page contains practice questions divided by topic. Use these pages to work out your child's strengths and the areas they find tricky. The questions get harder down each page.

Assessment tests

The second half of the book contains six assessment tests, each with a mix of question types from the first half of the book. They take a similar form to the real test.

- You can print off multiple-choice answer sheets from our website, www.cgplearning.co.uk/11+, so your child can practise taking the tests as if they're sitting the real thing.

- If you want to give your child timed practice, give them a time limit of 35 minutes for each test, and ask them to work as quickly and carefully as they can.

- Your child should aim for a mark of around 85% (26 questions correct) in each test. If they score less than this, use their results to work out the areas they need more practice on.

- If they haven't managed to finish the test in time, they need to work on increasing their speed, whereas if they have made a lot of mistakes, they need to work more carefully.

- Keep track of your child's scores using the progress chart on the inside back cover of the book.

Published by CGP

Editors:
Luke Antieul, David Broadbent, Sharon Keeley-Holden, Sarah Williams

Contributors:
Sue Foord, John Hawkins, Julie Hunt, Katrina Saville

With thanks to Rachel Murray and Glenn Rogers for the proofreading.

ISBN: 978 1 84762 826 8
Printed by Elanders Ltd, Newcastle upon Tyne
Clipart from Corel®

Based on the classic CGP style created by Richard Parsons.

CONTENTS

Place Value

For each row of numbers below, circle the number that is the smallest.

1.   165   95   120   180   (50)

2.   3000   (890)   2450   1900   980

3.   120   174   131   (114)   128

4.   (1230)   3420   2030   1440   2620

5.   4.2   2.7   (3.1)   3.5   2.4

/ 5

What number is the arrow pointing to on each of these number lines?

6.   10 ─── 15 ─── 20   Answer: 14

7.   0 ─── 10 ─── 20   Answer: 16

8.   45 ─── 70 ─── 95   Answer: 80

9.   14 ─────── 24   Answer: 12

/ 5

10. 30 ─────── 80   Answer: 65

Write down whether the 7 in each of the following numbers stands for hundreds, tens, units, tenths or hundredths.

11. 710   Answer: tens

12. 627.4   Answer: tenths

13. 7.36   Answer: hundreds

14. 26.71   Answer: units

/ 5

15. 14.27   Answer: hundredths

Place Value

16. Rearrange the digits in 2753 to make the largest number possible.

    Answer: 7532

17. Josephine timed how long each member of her family spent brushing their teeth. She recorded the results in this table. Who brushed their teeth in the shortest time?

    Answer: John

Name	Time (seconds)
Dad	138
Mum	146
John	108
Natalie	155
Karen	114

18. The heights of 5 children were measured. Their heights were 1.21 m, 1.12 m, 1.20 m, 1.02 m and 1.10 m. What was the height of the shortest person?   Answer: 1.02   m

19. Circle the number that is exactly halfway between 2.4 and 3.8.

    A   3.0   **B**   3.2   **C**   2.9   **D**   2.6   **E**   3.1

20. Mr Pearson is catching a plane. His luggage weighs 20.08 kg. How many of these airlines would let him take his luggage on the plane?

    Answer: 3

Airline	Maximum luggage weight (kg)
Air Kings	20.2
Fast Flights	19.95
Fly by Night	20.14
Pronto Planes	20.4
Speedy Jet	20.05

21. Which of these pairs of numbers are the same distance from 19? Circle the correct answer.

    A   12 and 24   **C**   16 and 21   **E**   14 and 25

    B   17 and 22   **D**   15 and 23

22. Circle the number which is closest to 1000.

    A   996.7   **B**   1004.1   **C**   1002.9   **D**   996.3   **E**   997.5

23. 6 is exactly halfway between one of these pairs of numbers. Circle the correct pair.

    A   6.7 and 5.7   **C**   6.1 and 5.7   **E**   6.6 and 5.3

    B   6.4 and 5.6   **D**   6.8 and 5.5

    / 8

Section One — Number Knowledge

Rounding Up and Down

Round the following numbers to the nearest 10.

1. 71   Answer: _3_____

2. 349   Answer: _350_____

3. 407   Answer: _4‍0‍0_____

4. 1536   Answer: _1540_____

5. 3092   Answer: _3 90_____   / 5

Round 1295.61 to:

6. the nearest 100.   Answer: _129561_____

7. the nearest tenth.   Answer: _12956.1_____

8. the nearest 10.   Answer: _129561_____

9. the nearest whole number. Answer: _129561_____   / 4

Write down whether these numbers have been rounded to the nearest 10, 100 or 1000:

10. 25 rounded to 30.   Answer: _10_____

11. 381 rounded to 400.   Answer: _100_____

12. 615 rounded to 620.   Answer: _100_____

13. 1247 rounded to 1000.   Answer: _1000_____

14. 517.4 rounded to 500.   Answer: _10_____   /5

15. Anya has £6.27 in her purse. What is
    £6.27 rounded to the nearest pound?   Answer: £ _6.00_____

16. There are 212 fish in an aquarium.
    How many fish are there to the nearest 10?   Answer: _210_____

17. 3264 people attended a rugby match.
    How many is this to the nearest 100?   Answer: _3300_____   / 3

Section One — Number Knowledge

Rounding Up and Down

18. Jan runs a market stall. She decides to round all of her prices to the nearest 10p. Which two items will now be cheaper? Circle the correct answer.

    A   potatoes and cauliflower
    B   tomatoes and runner beans
    C   cabbage and tomatoes
    D   runner beans and cauliflower
    E   cabbage and cauliflower

Item	Price
Potatoes	76p
Cauliflower	£1.15
Tomatoes	93p
Runner beans	47p
Cabbage	84p

19. The path around Mo's garden is 1265 cm. Round this length to the nearest 10 cm.

    Answer: 1270 cm

20. A book weighs 159.53 g. What is this weight rounded to the nearest whole number?

    Answer: 159.53 g

21. Josie is 147.5 cm tall and Martina is 145.3 cm tall. They both round their height to the nearest 10 cm. Which of these statements is true? Circle the correct answer.

    A   Josie's rounded height is greater than Martina's rounded height.
    B   Martina and Josie have the same rounded height.
    C   Josie's height is rounded to 148 cm.
    D   Martina's height is rounded to 140 cm.
    E   Martina's height is rounded to 100 cm.

22. The town of Thelston has a population of 6000, rounded to the nearest 1000. Circle the number that could not be the actual number of people living in Thelston.

    A   5621   B   5495   C   6497   D   6010   E   6318

23. Ben's dad weighs 78.49 kg. What is his weight rounded to the nearest 0.1 kg?

    Answer: 7.849 kg

24. Which of these is equal to 650? Circle the correct answer.

    A   626.5 to the nearest 10   D   650.7 to the nearest whole number
    B   6490 to the nearest 100   E   646.1 to the nearest 10
    C   657.2 to the nearest 10

/ 7

Section One — Number Knowledge

Number Knowledge

For each row of numbers below, circle the lowest value.

1. (0.7)   6   0.2   1   3

2. 3   (−6)   1   0   −2

Complete each statement using a < or > sign.

3. −5 __>__ −9

4. 2 __>__ −4

Hint: < means 'is less than' and > means 'is greater than'.

5. −3 __<__ 0

/ 5

6. This table shows the maximum temperature each morning for 5 days. What is the difference between the highest and lowest temperatures recorded?

Answer: ____b____ °C

Day	Temperature (°C)
Monday	-3
Tuesday	0
Wednesday	2
Thursday	-2
Friday	-1

7. Which of these statements is false? Circle the correct answer.

   A   49 + 17 will give an even number.

   B   34 − 18 will give an even number.

   C   17 + 12 will give an odd number.

   D   (6 × 6 will give an even number.)

   E   19 − 9 will give an odd number.

8. Jacob starts at −26 and subtracts 22. What number does Jacob end up at?   Answer: __4__

9. Which number is in the wrong section of this Venn diagram?

   Answer: __1__

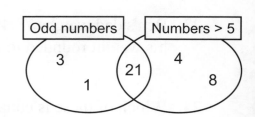

10. Circle the number below that is even and greater than −3.

    1   7   -6   2   5

/ 5

Section One — Number Knowledge

Number Knowledge

11. Rabin's age is equal to the sum of the first
    three multiples of 4. How old is Rabin?   Answer: _12_

12. Circle the number that is not a factor of 48.

    A 8   **B** 4   **C** 12   **D** 6   **(E** 9**)**

13. Circle the number which is a multiple of 6 and 9.

    A 30   **B** 12   **(C** 18**)**   **D** 27   **E** 3

14. Constance thinks of a number. It is the sum of all of the
    odd numbers between 0 and 10. What is her number?   Answer: _5_

15. There are 36 children at a party. They all split into equal
    teams to play some games. Which of these cannot be the
    number of children in each team? Circle the correct answer.

    Hint: The number of children on each team must be a factor of 36.

    A 6   **B** 3   **C** 4   **D** 9   **(E** 8**)**

16. Cathy says that all multiples of 3 are odd numbers.
    Dolly says that all multiples of 4 are even numbers.
    Ellie says that all multiples of 2 are also multiples of 4.
    Which of the statements below is true? Circle the correct answer.

    A   Only Ellie is correct.   **D**   Ellie and Dolly are both correct.

    B   Cathy and Dolly are both correct.   **E**   Only Dolly is correct.

    C   Cathy, Dolly and Ellie are all correct.

17. Which set of labels is missing from the sorting table? Circle the correct answer.

	odd numbers	even numbers
?	3, 5	6
?	7	4, 8

    A   factors of 15; not factors of 15

    B   multiples of 3; not multiples of 3

    C   less than 6; 6 or more

    D   factors of 30; not factors of 30

    E   less than 5; 5 or more

18. Circle the set of numbers which contains only multiples of 2 or 5.

    2, 10, 13   3, 4, 15   16, 20, 25   12, 13, 14   **(25, 30, 33)**

    / 8

Section One — Number Knowledge

Number Sequences

Write down the next number in each of the sequences below.

1. 7, 10, 13, 16...   Answer: _19_

2. 6, 12, 18, 24...   Answer: _30_

3. 28, 26, 24, 22...   Answer: _30_

4. 8.5, 9, 9.5, 10...   Answer: _1.6_

5. 1, 2, 4, 8...   Answer: _96_

/ 5

The students in Year 4 are making number sequences.
What is the 3rd number in each person's sequence?

6. Tariq starts at 2 and counts on in steps of 3.
    Answer: _5_

Hint: To find the numbers in a sequence, you can draw a number line and use it to help you count on or back.

7. Michelle starts at 8 and counts on in steps of 6.
    Answer: _14_

8. Harpreet starts at 0 and counts on in steps of 0.5.
    Answer: _0_

9. Paul starts at 20 and counts back in steps of 6.
    Answer: _13_

10. Gabrielle starts at 36 and counts back in steps of 5.
    Answer: _31_

/ 5

Write down the missing number in each of the sequences below.

11. 5,   10,   15, _20_ ,   25

12. 9,   13,   17,   21,   _25_

13. 52, _54_ ,   56,   58,   60

14. 45,   42,   _39_ ,   36,   33

15. _49_ ,   42,   35,   28,   21

/ 5

Number Sequences

16. Klara starts at 18 and counts on in steps of 6.
    Circle the number which will be in her sequence.

    A 34   **B** 35   **C** 36   **D** 37   **E** 38

17. The diagram shows the tiles on Mr Aston's roof.
    In each row there is 1 more tile than in the previous row.
    How many tiles will he have in the 6th row?

    Answer: 6

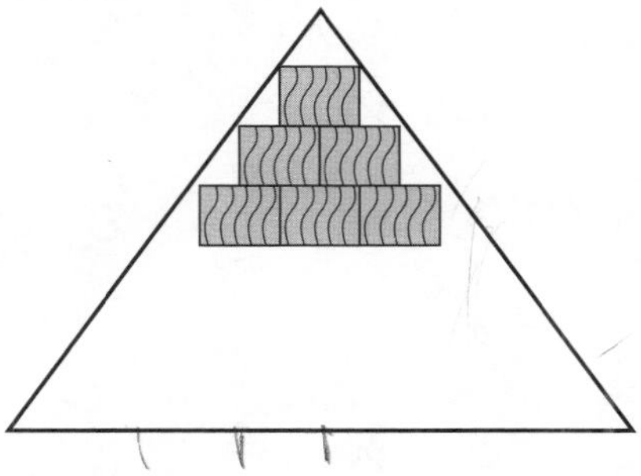

18. Nilesh writes down a sequence starting at 16. He counts back in steps of 3.
    Circle the number that will not be in his sequence.

    7   3   4   1   10

19. Caitlin starts at 10 and counts on in steps of 2.5.
    Circle the number that will be in her sequence.

    16.5   18   17.5   14   13.5

20. Charlie started at 7 and used the rule "subtract 5" to make a sequence.
    What is the 4th number in his sequence? Circle the correct answer.

    A −3   **B** −7   **C** 2   **D** −2   **E** −8

21. Jesper writes a sequence of numbers with the rule:

    Add the last two numbers together.

    The first five numbers in the sequence are:
        1, 2, 3, 5, 8
    What is the 7th number in Jesper's sequence?   Answer: 10

22. Molly writes a sequence using the rule "add 5". She starts at 2.
    Circle the number that will be in her sequence.

    A 27   **B** 28   **C** 29   **D** 30   **E** 31

23. Gina is using a sequence to plant seeds in some plant pots. She plants
    1 seed in the 1st pot, 4 seeds in the 2nd pot, 7 seeds in the 3rd pot
    and so on. Circle the number of seeds she will plant in the 5th pot.

    A 9   **B** 10   **C** 7   **D** 13   **E** 12

    / 8

Section One — Number Knowledge

Fractions

A fraction of each of these shapes is shaded. Write down the letter of the shape that matches each fraction.

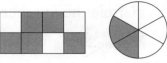

1. ½   Answer: _E_

2. ¾   Answer: _C_

3. ²⁄₆   Answer: _B_

4. ⅕   Answer: _D_

5. ⅝   Answer: _A_

A   **B**

C   **D**   **E**

/ 5

6. There are 16 sweets in a bag. Lakshmi eats ¼ of the sweets. How many sweets does Lakshmi eat?   Answer: _2⁄8_

7. What fraction of the rectangle is shaded? Circle the correct answer.

   A ³⁄₁₂   **B** ⁵⁄₁₂   **C** ⁸⁄₁₂   **D** ⁷⁄₁₂   **E** ⁶⁄₁₂

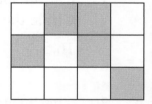

8. Which letter shows where the fraction ¾ should be placed on this number line? Circle the correct answer.

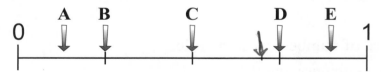

9. A bag of crisps is normally 60p. How much do the crisps cost under this special offer?

   Answer: _40_____ p

   ┌─────────────────────┐
   │   Special Offer   │
   │ Crisps are ⅓ of   │
   │ the normal price. │
   └─────────────────────┘

10. ¼ of the circle on the right is shaded. Which of the circles below has an equal amount shaded? Circle the correct answer.

Hint: Fractions with different numerators and denominators can be equal in value.

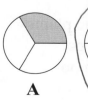 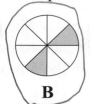

   A   **B**   **C**   **D**   **E**

/ 5

Section One — Number Knowledge

Fractions and Decimals

Write the fractions below as decimals.

1. ½   Answer: 1.2

2. ¼   Answer: 1.4

3. ¹⁄₁₀   Answer: 1.10

4. ¾   Answer: 3.4

5. ⁸⁄₁₀   Answer: 8.10

Circle the largest value in each row.

6. 0.8   ½   0.2   (0.75)   ¼

7. ⁶⁄₁₀   ¾   (½)   0.4   0.5

8. ¼   0.2   0.1   ¹⁄₁₀   ²⁄₁₀

9. ⁷⁄₁₀ of this shape is shaded. What is this value as a decimal?

Answer: 0.7

10. Joyce shared £1.00 with her two sisters. Annette got £0.10, Elizabeth got £0.50 and Joyce kept £0.40. What fraction of the money did Elizabeth get?   Answer: 0.10

11. Micah eats ²⁄₄ of a pizza and Rose eats ¼. Which of the following decimals shows the amount of pizza left over? Circle the correct answer.

   A 0.2   **B** 0.5   **C** (0.4)   **D** 0.6   **E** 0.25

12. The table shows the amount of a cake eaten by four people. Who ate ³⁄₁₀ of the cake?

   Answer: Susan

Name	Amount of cake eaten
Kelly	0.1
Bethan	0.35
Susan	0.3
Gurpreet	0.25

13. How many quarters are there in 0.75?

   Answer: 3

Section One — Number Knowledge

Addition

Write down the answer to each calculation.

1. 33 + 9   Answer: 42

2. 23 + 47   Answer: 70

3. 85 + 16   Answer: 101

4. 65 + 48   Answer: 113

/ 4

Write down the answer to each calculation.

5. 211 + 54   Answer: 265

6. 38 + 340   Answer: 378

7. 685 + 19   Answer: 704

8. 507 + 182   Answer: 689

/ 4

What is the total cost of buying the following items?

Hat	£2.20
Scarf	£7.40
Shirt	£12.30
Jumper	£15.50
Jacket	£22.50

9. A jacket and a hat.   Answer: £ 24.70

10. A scarf and a jumper.   Answer: £ 22.90

11. A scarf and a jacket.   Answer: £ 22.10

12. A shirt and a scarf.   Answer: £ 19.70

13. A jumper and a shirt.   Answer: £ 27.80

/ 5

14. Mel has 45 tulips in her front garden and 46 tulips in her back garden. How many tulips does Mel have in total?   Answer: 91

15. Mr Black grows two melons weighing 320 g and 446 g. How much do they weigh altogether?   Answer: 766 g

16. Jane buys garden ornaments weighing 315 g and 350 g. What is their total weight?

    Answer: 665 g

/ 3

Addition

17. Two planks of wood measuring 133 cm and 327 cm are laid end to end. What is the total length of the planks?   Answer: _460_ cm

18. What is 199 + 178?   Answer: _377_

19. What is the total of all of the numbers on this spinner?

    Answer: _39_

20. 191 parents and 216 children went to a school concert. How many people went to the concert in total?   Answer: _457_

21. Which of these additions equals 90? Circle the correct answer.

    A   71 + 21   **C**   57 + 33   **E**   43 + 37

    B   45 + 55   **D**   24 + 56

22. John ran two races in 152 seconds and 147 seconds. What was his total time for both races?   Answer: _____ s

23. 336 Barchester City fans and 582 Dartfield fans were at a football match. How many fans were there altogether? Circle the correct answer.

    A   958   **B**   918   **C**   988   **D**   888   **E**   998

24. Jake had fish and chips at the café. How much did he spend?

    Answer: £ _3.71_

Café Menu	
Chicken	£3.59
Fish	£2.46
Chips	£1.25
Peas	45p
Beans	35p

    2.00
    177

25. Add together 25, 85, 54 and 58.

    Answer: _202_

/ 9

Section Two — Working with Numbers

Subtraction

Write down the answer to each calculation.

1. 73 – 12   Answer: 61

2. 69 – 34   Answer: 35

3. 100 – 47   Answer: 53

4. 125 – 77   Answer: _____

$$\begin{array}{r} 1\overset{11}{2}5 \\ 77 \\ \hline 8 \\ 1 \end{array}$$

Use each of the numbers in the box once to complete the calculations below.

87	126	49	24	121

5. 198 – 72 = 126

6. 249 – 225 = 24

7. 123 – 87 = 36

8. 166 – 49 = 45

9. 71 – 49 = 22

Hint: For questions 7-9, you need to subtract the result of the calculation from the number you've been given.

10. John spends 78p. How much change will he get from £1?

Answer: _____ p

11. Alisha spends £3.50. How much change will she get from £5?

Answer: £ _____

12. Kate spends £2.60. How much change will she get from £5?

Answer: £ _____

13. Sita spends £4.30. How much change will she get from £10?

Answer: £ _____

14. Perry spends £7.85. How much change will he get from £10?

Answer: £ _____

Subtraction

15. There were 132 people in a theatre. 16 people left during the interval. How many people were left in the theatre?   Answer: _____

16. Which two numbers have a difference of 23? Circle the correct answer.

    A   32 and 15   **C**   67 and 24   **E**   43 and 25

    B   56 and 39   **D**   71 and 48

17. A pond was filled with 167 litres of water but 45 litres leaked out. How much water was left in the pond?   Answer: _____ l

18. Mr Farr has a 300 cm piece of wood. He saws off 172 cm. What is the length of the remaining piece?   Answer: _____ cm

19. 98 men and 265 women visited the local gym. How many more women went to the gym than men?   Answer: _____

20. Terri has 387 points on a computer game but she loses 136 points. What is her final score? Circle the correct answer.

    A   523   **B**   251   **C**   257   **D**   243   **E**   351

21. Mr Samson enters three sunflowers in the local flower show. They are 178 cm, 213 cm and 163 cm tall. What is the difference in height between the shortest sunflower and the tallest sunflower? Circle the correct answer.

    A   350 cm   **B**   165 cm   **C**   50 cm   **D**   43 cm   **E**   52 cm

22. Patrick wants to buy a game costing £10.00. He has saved £6.65. How much more money does he need to save? Circle the correct answer.

    A   £3.45   **B**   £4.45   **C**   £6.15   **D**   £3.35   **E**   £2.55

23. $317 - 38 = \boxed{}$

    Circle the missing number in this calculation.

    /9

    A   387   **B**   279   **C**   287   **D**   289   **E**   278

Section Two — Working with Numbers

Multiplying and Dividing by 10 and 100

Fill in the gaps to complete the calculations below.

1. 70 × 10 = _____

2. 62 × 10 = _____

3. 28 × 100 = _____

4. 510 ÷ 10 = _____

5. 6000 ÷ 100 = _____

6. Farmer Joe's chickens lay 15 eggs every day.
    How many eggs will they have laid after 10 days?

    Answer: _____

7. Crisps cost 72p per packet. There are 10 packets in every box.
    What is the price of each box? Give your answer in pence.

    Answer: _____ p

8. Tickets for a school concert cost £10. The school sold £6210 worth
    of tickets. How many tickets were sold? Circle the correct answer.

    A 6210   **B** 621   **C** 62100   **D** 6.21   **E** 62

9. Jake has a plank of wood that is 500 cm long. He cuts the plank of wood into 10
    equal pieces. How many centimetres long is each piece? Circle the correct answer.

    A 500 cm   **B** 0.5 cm   **C** 5 cm   **D** 50 cm   **E** 5000 cm

10. ☐ ÷ 10 = 44

    Circle the missing number in this calculation.

    A 44   **B** 4   **C** 4400   **D** 440   **E** 140

Multiplication

The cost of some items in a shop are shown below.

Book £5   CD £7   Teddy Bear £6   Football £4

Work out how much each person spends.

1. Mabel buys 5 books.   Answer: £ _____

2. Mohammed buys 4 CDs.   Answer: £ _____

3. Phillip buys 6 teddy bears.   Answer: £ _____

4. Naomi buys 8 footballs.   Answer: £ _____

5. Bryony buys 9 CDs.   Answer: £ _____

/ 5

Write down the answer to each calculation.

6. 30×4 Answer: _____

7. 90×5 Answer: _____

8. 6×70 Answer: _____

9. 60×3 Answer: _____

10. 80×5 Answer: _____

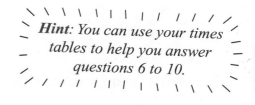

Hint: You can use your times tables to help you answer questions 6 to 10.

/ 5

Write down the answer to each calculation.

11. 15×6 Answer: _____

12. 27×3 Answer: _____

13. 43×5 Answer: _____

14. 36×4 Answer: _____

15. 5×45 Answer: _____

/ 5

Multiplication

16. $\boxed{4} \times 9 = 36$

    What is the missing number in this calculation?   Answer: _____4_____

17. Ross buys eight packs of stickers. Each pack contains six stickers. How many stickers does he buy in total?   Answer: _____48_____

18. Mrs Robinson has a roll of ribbon. She cuts it into seven parts that are 5 m long each. How long was the roll of ribbon?   Answer: _____35_____ m

19. A teacher marks 30 test papers. There are nine questions on each paper. How many questions does she mark in total?   Answer: _____270_____

20. Which of the following calculations is correct? Circle the correct answer.

    A $6 \times 7 = 42$ **C** $6 \times 9 = 63$ **E** $7 \times 7 = 48$

    B $9 \times 8 = 56$ **D** $9 \times 5 = 50$

21. What is the total cost of three DVDs that cost 99p each? Circle the correct answer.

    A £3.00   **B** £3.03   **C** £2.97   **D** £2.91   **E** £3.09

22. A hospital orders 30 boxes of bandages. Each box contains seven bandages. How many bandages does the hospital order? Circle the correct answer.

    A 210   **B** 140   **C** 224   **D** 196   **E** 188

23. A postman drives 8 kilometres each day. He works for 23 days each month. How many kilometres does the postman drive each month?   Answer: _____184_____ km

24. One coach can seat 33 people. How many people can four coaches seat? Circle the correct answer.

    A 106   **B** 132   **C** 124   **D** 120   **E** 99

/9

Division

Write down the answer to each calculation.

1. $16 \div 2$ Answer: ___8___

2. $27 \div 3$ Answer: ___9___

3. $42 \div 6$ Answer: ___7___

4. $36 \div 6$ Answer: ___6___

5. $81 \div 9$ Answer: ___9___

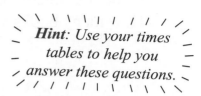

Hint: Use your times tables to help you answer these questions.

/ 5

Write down the remainder in each calculation.

6. $19 \div 2$ Answer: ___9 r1___

7. $46 \div 6$ Answer: ___7 r4___

8. $69 \div 9$ Answer: ___7___

9. $68 \div 5$ Answer: ___13 r2___

10. $88 \div 7$ Answer: ___12___

/ 5

Work out how much money each person will get.

11. £16 divided between 4 people.   Answer: £ _____

12. £75 divided between 5 people.   Answer: £ _____

13. £96 divided between 6 people.   Answer: £ _____

14. £128 divided between 4 people.   Answer: £ _____

15. £57 divided between 3 people.   Answer: £ _____

/ 5

Division

16. A bookshelf has three shelves. Jim divides
    69 books equally between the three shelves.
    How many books are there on each shelf?   Answer: _____

17. A box of 96 chocolates is divided equally between eight friends.
    How many chocolates does each friend get? Circle the correct answer.

    A   15   **B**   12   **C**   9   **D**   11   **E**   13

18. Farmer Giles has 86 eggs. He packs them into boxes of 6.
    How many eggs does he have left over?   Answer: _____

19. Look at the calculations given below. Circle the calculation that is incorrect.

    A $125 \div 5 = 25$ **C** $58 \div 7 = 8$ **E** $121 \div 11 = 11$

    B $72 \div 6 = 12$ **D** $350 \div 5 = 70$

20. Which of these numbers can be exactly divided by four? Circle the correct answer.

    A   50   **B**   87   **C**   58   **D**   60   **E**   73

21. $68 \div 9 = \boxed{7}$ remainder 5

    What is the missing number in this calculation?   Answer: _____

22. Phoebe has 79 coins in her coin collection. She places
    all of the coins in an album. Each page of the album
    holds seven coins. How many pages will she need to
    fit all 79 coins in her album?   Answer: _____

23. June has 39 brownies. She divides all of the brownies equally
    between four boxes but she has some left over. How many
    brownies does she have left over? Circle the correct answer.

    A   1   **B**   2   **C**   3   **D**   4   **E**   5

    / 8

Word Problems

1. Beth spent £2.50 on two mugs of hot chocolate and one banana milkshake. The banana milkshake cost 50p. How much did each mug of hot chocolate cost?

   Answer: £ _____

2. Mr Warren brought 10 boxes of fizzy sweets to a school party. Each box contained 128 fizzy sweets. How many fizzy sweets did Mr Warren bring in total?

   Answer: _____

3. Darren bought 4 chews and 1 chocolate mouse from the tuck shop. How much did Darren pay?

   Answer: _____ p

Tuck Shop Prices	
Chews	8p each
Lollies	10p each
Chocolate mice	12p each
Jelly worms	6p each

4. Waleed paid £20 for six cinema tickets. He received £2 in change. How much did each cinema ticket cost?

   Answer: £ _____

5. Jodie wants to buy a jacket that costs £40, but she only has £20. She saves £4 each week until she has enough money to buy the jacket. How many weeks did she need to save for? Circle the correct answer.

   A 5   **B** 10   **C** 7   **D** 4   **E** 8

6. Callum thinks of a number. He divides it by 4 and ends up with 6. What number did Callum start with? Circle the correct answer.

   A 24   **B** 18   **C** 15   **D** 1.5   **E** 12

7. William has £10 to spend on his mum's birthday presents. Which of the following would cost exactly £10? Circle the correct answer.

   A 2 scarves and 1 plant.
   B 2 bottles of perfume.
   C 1 bottle of perfume and 2 scarves.
   D 2 plants and 1 scarf.
   E 1 plant and 1 bottle of perfume.

   Plant £5

   Perfume £7

   Scarf £1.50

8. Nicola's dad is exactly 6 times as old as she is. Which of these is her dad's age? Circle the correct answer.

   A 32   **B** 36   **C** 41   **D** 28   **E** 38

   / 8

Word Problems

9. Mr Bracken paid £15 for 10 litres of petrol for his car.
    He used 6 litres of petrol to drive to his aunt's house.
    How much did the petrol for this journey cost?   Answer: £ _____

10. Robin multiplies 3 by 8 and divides the answer by 6. Arjen also starts with 3,
    but does a different calculation. Both boys get the same answer.
    Which of these calculations could Arjen have done? Circle the correct answer.

    A   Multiply a number by 4 then divide by 3.

    B   Multiply a number by 16 then divide by 2.

    C   Multiply a number by 4 then divide by 2.

    D   Multiply a number by 2 then divide by 4.

    E   Multiply a number by 2 then divide by 3.

11. Mrs Price is making costumes for a play. She can make
    3 rabbit costumes and 2 squirrel costumes from 5 metres
    of fabric. How many metres of fabric will she need to
    make 9 rabbit costumes and 6 squirrel costumes?   Answer: _____ m

12. The table shows the ingredients used to make pasta
    carbonara for 4 people. How much pasta would be
    needed for exactly 5 people?

    Answer: _____ g

Pasta Carbonara (serves 4)	
Pasta	400 g
Cream	100 ml
Ham	100 g
Shallots	2

13. Yolanda pays for 6 books using two £15 book tokens.
    The books are all the same price and she gets no change.
    How much does each book cost?   Answer: £ _____

14. A pack of butter weighs 200 g and is 4 cm tall. Penny places packs of butter
    on top of each other to make a stack that is 12 cm tall. What is the weight of
    the stack of butter? Circle the correct answer.

    A   800 g   C   12 g   E   48 g

    B   200 g   D   600 g

    *Hint: Start by working
    out the number of packs
    of butter in the stack.*

15. Hair clips cost £1.50 each. How many hair
    clips can Martha afford to buy with £10?

    Answer: _____

/ 7

Section Three — Word Problems

Data Tables

Look at the school uniform order form.
Use the form to answer these questions.

School Uniform Order Form		
Item	Price (each)	Number Ordered
Shirt	£5.99	3
Trousers	£10.99	1
Jumper	£12.99	1
Shorts	£5.99	2
Blazer	£19.99	1

1.   How many shirts have been ordered?

Answer: _____

2.   Which item costs £12.99?

Answer: _____

3.   What is the most expensive item of uniform?

Answer: _____

4.   Which item has been ordered twice?   Answer: _____

5.   How many items have been ordered in total?   Answer: _____

/ 5

6.   The table shows the number of pets owned by the children in Class D.

Number of pets owned	1	2	3	4	5
Number of children	7	8	3	4	3

How many children own two pets?   Answer: _____

7.   The table shows information about four towns. Which two towns have the same
number of shops and the same number of parks? Circle the correct answer.

A   Dellville and Coalton

B   Herdnell and Dellville

C   Coalton and Nolanbeck

D   Dellville and Nolanbeck

E   Herdnell and Nolanbeck

Town	Population	Number of shops	Number of parks
Herdnell	16 500	112	4
Dellville	28 000	136	6
Coalton	35 500	207	6
Nolanbeck	28 000	112	4

8.   The table shows the number of boys and
girls in Years 4 and 5 at Westfield School.
What is the total number of children in Year 5?

	Girls	Boys	Total
Year 4	13	12	25
Year 5	17	14	?

Answer: _____

/ 3

Data Tables

9. The table shows the temperature of the water in Tony's bath over a 3 hour period. Between which two times did the temperature fall by 5 °C? Circle the correct answer.

Time	Temperature (°C)
12:00	42
12:30	39
13:00	34
13:30	30
14:00	28
14:30	25
15:00	21

   A   12:00 and 12:30   **D**   14:00 and 14:30

   B   12:30 and 13:00   **E**   14:30 and 15:00

   C   13:00 and 13:30

10. 40 children were asked how they travel to school. The results are shown in the table.

	Car	Bus	Bike	Train	Walk
Number of children	8	3	6	2	21

How many children did not travel to school by car? Circle the correct answer.

A 26   **B** 32   **C** 19   **D** 8   **E** 22

11. Mrs Chung is putting her shopping bill into this table. How many onions did she buy?

Answer: _____

Item	Number Bought	Cost (per item)	Total Cost
Cereal	2	£2.60	£5.20
Milk	1	£1.90	£1.90
Baked Beans	4	70p	£2.80
Onions	?	20p	£1.40

Marks	Boys	Girls
0 – 20	2	1
21 – 40	3	4
41 – 60	2	8
61 – 80	10	?
81 – 100	3	2

12. 20 boys and 20 girls did a maths test. Some of their marks are shown in the table. How many girls scored 61-80 marks?

Answer: _____

Item	Number sold		
	Morning	Afternoon	Total
Doughnuts		10	26
Cookies	7	11	18
Brownies	?	24	

Hint: Start by working out the number of doughnuts sold in the morning.

13. A bakery started to record the number of items it sold in one day in this table. They sold 30 items altogether in the morning. How many brownies did they sell in the morning?

Answer: _____

/ 5

Displaying Data

Mr Potter made this bar chart to show how many tomatoes he picked each day.
Use the bar chart to answer questions 1-4.

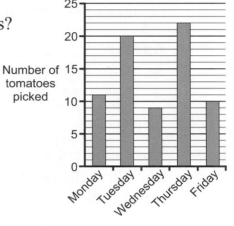

1. On which day did Mr Potter pick the most tomatoes?

   Answer: _____

2. On which day were 10 tomatoes picked?

   Answer: _____

3. How many tomatoes were picked on Monday?

   Answer: _____

4. What was the total number of tomatoes picked on Thursday and Friday?

   Answer: _____

5. Shirley made this pictogram to show
   the different buttons that she found
   in her drawer. How many red buttons
   did she find? Circle the correct answer.

   A 2.5   **D** 3
   B 12   **E** 10
   C 4

Button colour	Number of buttons
White	⊙ ⊙ ⊙ ⊙ ⊙
Red	⊙ ⊙ ◖
Black	⊙ ⊙ ⊙ ⊙

⊙ = 4 buttons

6. The bar chart shows the number
   of ice creams sold from an ice cream
   van over six months. In which month
   were 300 ice creams sold?

   Answer: _____

7. Alexa counted the number of chickens,
   ducks and turkeys she saw at a farm.
   The pictogram shows her results.
   How many more ducks did she see than turkeys?

   Answer: _____

Chickens	🥚 🥚 🥚 🥚
Ducks	🥚 🥚 🥚
Turkeys	🥚 ◖

🥚 = 6 birds

/ 3

Section Four — Data Handling

Displaying Data

8. Jeremy made this chart to show the amount of piano practice he did each day. How many minutes of practice did he do in total?

Answer: _____ minutes

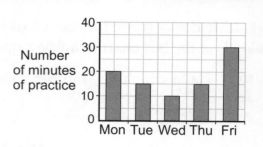

9. The pictogram shows the number of goals scored by Milton United in their matches. In how many matches did they score 2 or more goals?

Answer: _____

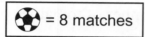

10. The bar chart shows the amount of sport played each week by a group of children. Which of the following sentences is true? Circle the correct answer.

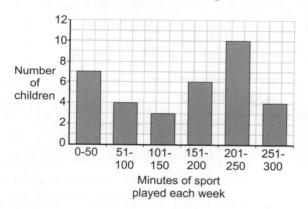

A 5 children play 251-300 minutes of sport.

B 8 children play less than 50 minutes of sport.

C Most of the children play 101-150 minutes of sport.

D 4 children play 251-300 minutes of sport.

E An even number of children play 0-50 minutes of sport.

11. 26 people voted for their favourite crisp flavour. Hans made a bar chart to show the results, but forgot to fill in the bar for prawn cocktail flavour. How many people voted for prawn cocktail?

Answer: _____

Hint: *Start by working out the total number of people who voted for the other three flavours.*

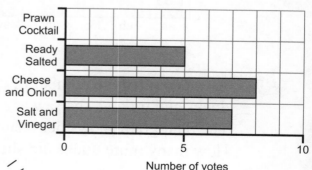

/ 4

Section Four — Data Handling

Angles

Look at the angles below and answer questions 1-4.

 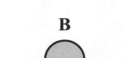   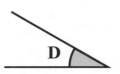

1. Which angle is exactly 90°?   Answer: _____

2. Which angle is smaller than 90°?   Answer: _____

3. Which angle is exactly 180°?   Answer: _____

4. Which angle is between 90° and 180°?   Answer: _____

/ 4

5. How many right angles are there in this shape? Circle the correct answer.

   A 0   **B** 1   **C** 2   **D** 3   **E** 4

6. The hour hand on this clock is pointing at 12. What number will the hour hand be pointing at if it turns 90° clockwise?

   Answer: _____

7. Circle the smallest angle.

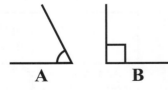   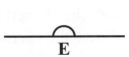

   A   **B**   **C**   **D**   **E**

8. Josie is facing south. She turns clockwise to face north. How many right angles has she turned through?

   Answer: _____

   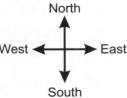

9. Estimate the size of angle *a*. Circle the correct answer.

   100°   45°   180°   90°   125°

   / 5

2D Shapes

Match each shape below to its description.

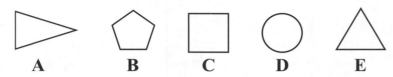

1. It is a shape with five sides and five corners.   Answer: _____

2. It is a shape with no corners.   Answer: _____

3. It has three equal sides and three equal angles.   Answer: _____

4. It is a triangle with only two equal sides.   Answer: _____

5. It has four equal sides and four right angles.   Answer: _____

/ 5

6. Which of these shapes is an equilateral triangle? Circle the correct answer.

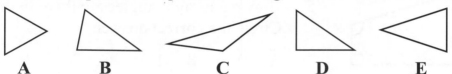

7. Which of these shapes is not a quadrilateral? Circle the correct answer.

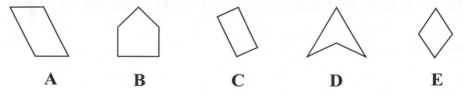

8. Which of these shapes should be placed into the shaded box of the sorting table? Circle the correct answer.

   A regular pentagon   **D** regular octagon
   B regular hexagon   **E** square
   C equilateral triangle

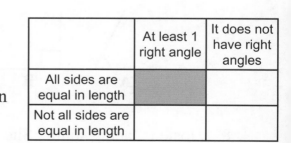

	At least 1 right angle	It does not have right angles
All sides are equal in length	▓	
Not all sides are equal in length		

9. Which of these shapes does not have any equal angles? Circle the correct answer.

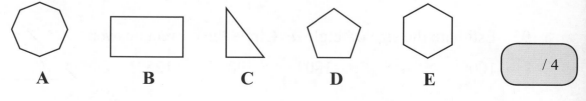

/ 4

Section Five — Shape and Space

2D Shapes — Area and Perimeter

Indira drew some shapes on squared paper.
The area of each square on the paper is 1 cm².

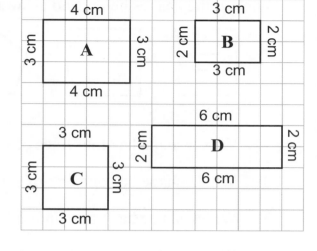

1. What is the perimeter of shape C?

   Answer: _____ cm

2. Which shape has a perimeter of 10 cm?

   Answer: _____

3. What is the area of shape D?

   Answer: _____ cm²

4. What is the area of shape C?   Answer: _____ cm²

5. What is the perimeter of shape A?   Answer: _____ cm

/ 5

6. A hexagon has six sides that are each 4 cm long.
   What is the perimeter of the hexagon?   Answer: _____ cm

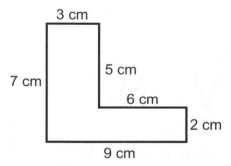

7. What is the perimeter of this shape?
   Circle the correct answer.

   A 30 cm   **C** 31 cm   **E** 29 cm

   B 28 cm   **D** 32 cm

8. Each square on this diagram has an area
   of 1 cm². What is the area of the triangle?

   Answer: _____ cm²

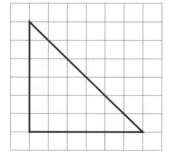

9. Mr Stiles has a rectangular vegetable patch with a perimeter
   of 28 m. The two longest sides are both 10 m long. What
   is the width of the vegetable patch? Circle the correct answer.

   A 8 m   **C** 3 m   **E** 4 m

   B 5 m   **D** 10 m

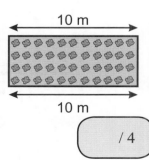

/ 4

Section Five — Shape and Space

Symmetry

Look at the shapes below and answer questions 1-5.

 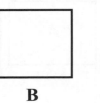 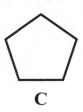 

  A   B   C   D   E

1. Which shape has four lines of symmetry?   Answer: _____

2. Which shape has one line of symmetry?   Answer: _____

3. Which shape has three lines of symmetry?   Answer: _____

4. Which shape has two lines of symmetry?   Answer: _____

5. Which shape has five lines of symmetry?   Answer: _____

/ 5

6. How many lines of symmetry does this rectangle have?

    Answer: _____

7. Which of the following letters has no lines of symmetry? Circle the correct answer.

M T D V N

8. The shape on the right is reflected in the vertical mirror line. Circle the option which shows the reflection of the shape.

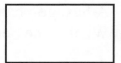

mirror line

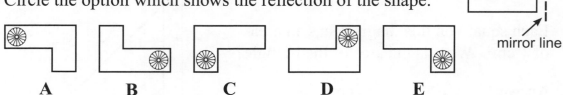

  A   B   C   D   E

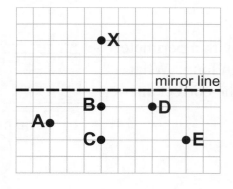

9. Point X is reflected in the horizontal mirror line. Which letter shows the position of its reflection? Circle the correct answer.

  A   B   C   D   E

/ 4

Section Five — Shape and Space

3D Shapes

Match each 3D shape below to its description.

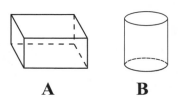 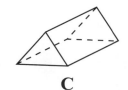

A   **B**   **C**   **D**   **E**

1.   A shape with 3 faces.   Answer: _____

2.   A shape with 6 faces and 12 edges.   Answer: _____

3.   A shape with 4 faces and 6 edges.   Answer: _____

4.   A shape with 5 faces and 9 edges.   Answer: _____

5.   A shape with 5 faces and 8 edges.   Answer: _____

/ 5

6.   Jack is making a gift box. He uses this net.
     Which 3D shape does Jack make? Circle the correct answer.

A pyramid   **C** cube   **E** sphere
B cone   **D** cylinder

7.   Ravi picks a 3D shape at random. It has 7 faces. Which of the
     following could be Ravi's shape? Circle the correct answer.

A   **B**   **C**   **D**   **E**

8.   Rebecca made a 3D shape from this net.
     What shape did she make? Circle the correct answer.

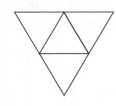

A cube   **D** triangle-based pyramid
B quadrilateral   **E** hexagonal prism
C triangular prism

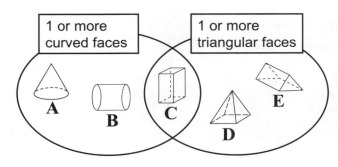

9.   Which shape should not
     be in the Venn diagram?
     Circle the correct answer.

A   **B**   **C**   **D**   **E**

/ 4

Section Five — Shape and Space

Shape Problems

Look at the shapes below and answer questions 1-5.

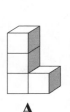 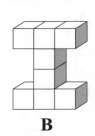 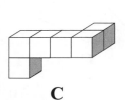 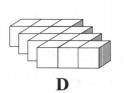 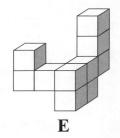

A **B** **C** **D** **E**

1. Which shape contains 4 cubes?   Answer: _____

2. Which shape contains 6 cubes?   Answer: _____

3. Which shape contains 8 cubes?   Answer: _____

4. Which shape contains 10 cubes?   Answer: _____

5. Which shape contains 12 cubes?   Answer: _____

/ 5

6. Chris fits two smaller shapes together to make shape X. Which two shapes did he use? Circle the correct answer.

X

Hint: You may have to reflect one of the shapes.

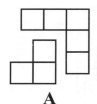 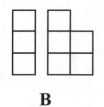 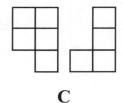 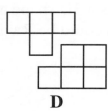 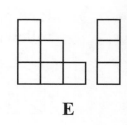

A **B** **C** **D** **E**

7. Dominic reflects the shape on the right in the mirror line. Which of the following shows the reflected shape? Circle the correct answer.

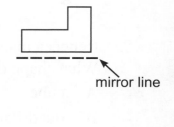

mirror line

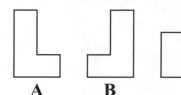

A **B** **C** **D** **E**

8. Which of these shapes is exactly the same shape as shape W? Circle the correct answer.

A **B** **C** **D** **E**

/ 3

Section Five — Shape and Space

Coordinates

Sasha drew some objects on a coordinate grid. Write down the coordinates of these objects:

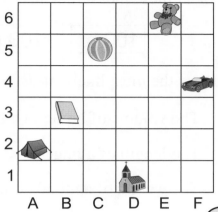

1. the book.   Answer: _____

2. the tent.   Answer: _____

3. the bear.   Answer: _____

4. the church.   Answer: _____

5. the car.   Answer: _____

Hint: Write your coordinates with the letter first and then the number.

/ 5

6. Carlos is drawing shapes on a coordinate grid. What shape has he drawn in the square B3? Circle the correct answer.

    A circle   **D** hexagon

    B star   **E** triangle

    C square

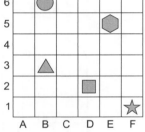

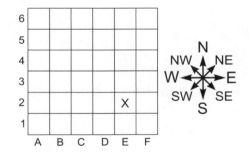

7. Karen is at point X. She travels 3 squares north and 4 squares south-west. What are the coordinates of the square that she reaches?

   Answer: _____

8. The coordinates of point A are (1, 2). What are the coordinates of point B? Circle the correct answer.

    A (3, 7)   **D** (7, 4)

    B (5, 9)   **E** (2, 6)

    C (3, 9)

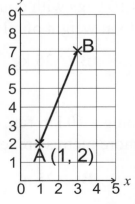

Hint: When you're writing coordinates, put the x-axis coordinate first and then the y-axis coordinate.

/ 3

Section Five — Shape and Space

Units

Look at these measurements.

| 100 m | 100 g | 0.3 litres | 5 ml | 7 cm |

Choose the most likely measurement for each of the following.

1. The volume of liquid in a full mug of tea.   Answer: _____

2. The length of a finger.   Answer: _____

3. The weight of a mobile phone.   Answer: _____

4. The volume of medicine in a teaspoonful.   Answer: _____

5. The length of a football pitch.   Answer: _____

/ 5

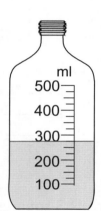

6. How much liquid is in the bottle on the left?

    Answer: _____ ml

7. Mrs Patel bought 30 cm of gold chain and 1.5 m of silver chain.
    How many centimetres of chain did she buy altogether?

    Answer: _____ cm

8. Lucas has some 500 ml bottles of cola. He pours them into a 2 litre jug.
    How many bottles are needed to fill the jug?

    Answer: _____

9. A baker fills 10 bags with doughnuts. Each bag of doughnuts weighs 350 g.
    What is the total weight of all the bags? Circle the correct answer.

    A   3.5 kg   **B**   35 kg   **C**   350 kg   **D**   35 g   **E**   3.5 g

10. Deepak is doing a 10 km run. He has run 9¾ km.
    How many more metres are left to run? Circle the correct answer.

    A   ¼ m   **B**   25 m   **C**   250 m   **D**   750 m   **E**   300 m

/ 5

Time

4:50	5:45	5:10	7:30	6:15
A	**B**	**C**	**D**	**E**

Write the letter of the time above that is the same as:

1.   Ten minutes to five.   Answer: _____

2.   Half past seven.   Answer: _____

3.   Quarter to six.   Answer: _____

4.   Half an hour earlier than quarter to seven.   Answer: _____

5.   Twenty minutes later than ten minutes to five.   Answer: _____

/ 5

6.   This timetable shows the times of buses
     going from Whitdale to the Hospital.
     Sarah needs to be at the Hospital at 11:00.
     What is the latest time that she can catch
     the bus from Whitdale? Circle the correct answer.

Whitdale	10:15	10:30	10:45
Thornby	10:25	10:40	10:55
Hospital	10:40	10:55	11:10

   A   10:15   **B**   10:30   **C**   10:45   **D**   10:40   **E**   10:55

7.   Jo goes on holiday on Tuesday 24th May.
     The last day of her holiday is the 13th June.
     How many weeks was she on holiday for?

Hint: Make sure you know how many days there are in each month.

     Answer: _____ weeks

8.   Lokesh starts his homework at 6:45 pm.
     He finishes it 70 minutes later.
     What time does he finish his homework?   Answer: _____:_____ pm

9.   Mrs Brown is going to a school concert.
     The concert starts at 3:15 pm. It takes her 35 minutes
     to drive to the school and 5 minutes to park her car and
     walk to the school. What time must she leave home?   Answer: _____:_____ pm

10. The time in Sydney, Australia, is 11 hours later than in the UK.
     When it is 10:15 am in the UK, what time is it in Sydney? Circle the correct answer.
     A   9:15 am   **C**   10:15 am   **E**   11:15 pm
     B   11:15 am   **D**   9:15 pm

/ 5

Section Six — Units and Measures

Mixed Problems

1. Which one of these shapes can be placed
    in the shaded area of the Venn diagram?
    Circle the correct answer.

    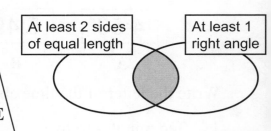

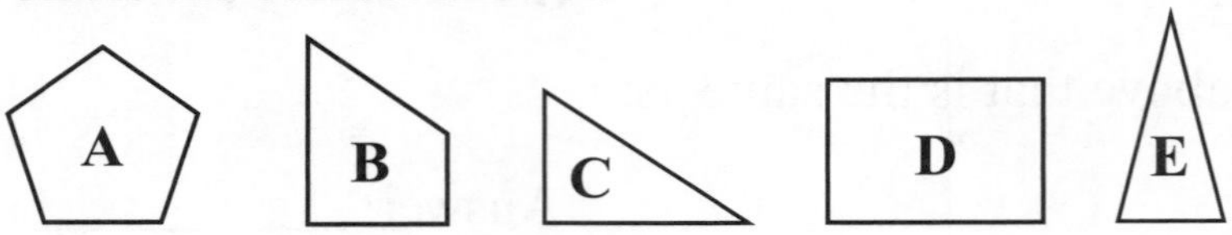

2. Anna worked for $4\frac{1}{2}$ hours on Saturday
    and $5\frac{1}{2}$ hours on Sunday. She is paid
    £4.50 for each hour of work.
    How much money did she earn in total?

    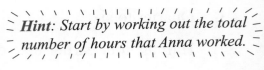

    Hint: Start by working out the total number of hours that Anna worked.

    Answer: £ _____

3. A 500 ml bottle of water costs 40p.
    How much will it cost to buy 3 litres of water?   Answer: £ _____

4. What fraction of these shapes have a line of symmetry? Circle the correct answer.

    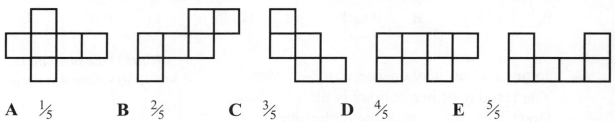

    A ⅕   **B** ⅖   **C** ⅗   **D** ⅘   **E** ⁵⁄₅

5. Hilda starts washing eight cars at 4:45 pm. It takes her 10 minutes to wash each car.
    What time will she finish washing the cars? Circle the correct answer.

    A   5:45 pm   **B**   5:05 pm   **C**   6:30 pm   **D**   5:30 pm   **E**   6:05 pm

6. Lucy runs 8 km in an hour.
    How many metres does she run in 15 minutes?   Answer: _____ m

7. Fran drew the shape on the right and reflected it in
    the mirror line. What is the total perimeter of the
    shape and its reflection? Circle the correct answer.

    A   24 cm   **C**   16 cm   **E**   20 cm
    B   28 cm   **D**   12 cm

    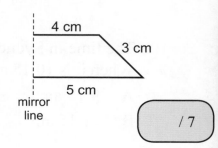

    / 7

Assessment Test 1

The rest of the book contains six assessment tests to help you improve your maths skills. Allow 35 minutes to do each test and work as quickly and as carefully as you can.

You can print **multiple-choice answer sheets** for these questions from our website — go to www.cgplearning.co.uk/11+. If you'd prefer to answer them in standard write-in format, either write your answers in the spaces provided or circle the **correct answer** from the options **A** to **E**.

1. Max has the following values of coins.
   How much money does he have?

A £3.90	**D** £3.54	
B £2.09	**E** £2.90	
C £3.09		

2. Pat and Imran are at the Post Office.
   They walk 2 squares north and 1 square east.

   Where do they walk to?

   A   Leisure Centre
   B   Library
   C   Supermarket
   D   Newsagent
   E   Sports Shop

   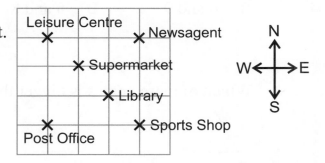

3. What is 295 rounded to the nearest 10?

   A   200   **B**   250   **C**   280   **D**   290   **E**   300

4. Hannah records the number of plants in her garden on a pictogram.

   How many bean plants does she have?

A 3	**C** 4	**E** 1½
B 5	**D** 2½	

   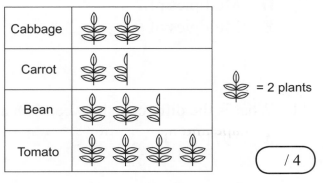

   / 4

Carry on to the next question → →

5. How many lines of symmetry does a regular pentagon have?

    A 4   **B** 7   **C** 6   **D** 5   **E** 8

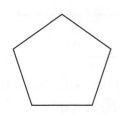

6. $7 \times 8 = 56$

    What is 7×80?

    A 73   **B** 490   **C** 650   **D** 560   **E** 87

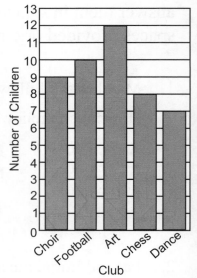

7. This chart shows how many children go to different clubs.

    How many more children go to art club than to dance club?

    Answer: _____

8. Which of the following pairs of numbers are factors of 36?

    A 4 and 8   **C** 7 and 12   **E** 6 and 7
    B 6 and 9   **D** 5 and 8

9. Which of these angles is bigger than 90°?

A

B

C

D
E

10. Which of these is the missing label from this Venn diagram?

    A Multiples of 11
    B Even numbers
    C Odd numbers
    D Multiples of 7
    E Multiples of 6

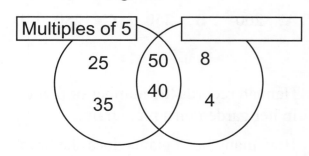

11. What is the difference between 998 and 1029?

    A 1971   **B** 31   **C** 32   **D** 28   **E** 2027

/ 7

Carry on to the next question → →

12. Julia buys some bags of biscuits for her dog. There are 8 biscuits in each bag.

   She gets 48 biscuits altogether. How many bags did she buy?

   Answer: _____

13. Each square in the shape on the right has an area of 1 cm². What is the area of the shape?

   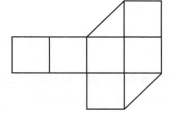

   | **A** | 7 cm² | **C** | 5 cm² | **E** | 8 cm² |
   | **B** | 5½ cm² | **D** | 6 cm² | | |

14. Jill recorded the temperature on five mornings. She put her results in this table.

   Which morning was coldest?

   Answer: _____

Day	Temperature
Monday	0 °C
Tuesday	2 °C
Wednesday	−1 °C
Thursday	−3 °C
Friday	−2 °C

15. What is the next number in this sequence?

   23   28   33   38   43   ?

   Answer: _____

16. What is 43 multiplied by 8?   Answer: _____

17. Look at the table on the right.

   How much carbohydrate and fat is there altogether in 100 g of bread?

   | **A** | 58 g | **C** | 52 g | **E** | 51 g |
   | **B** | 49 g | **D** | 36 g | | |

In 100 g of bread there is:	
Protein	9 g
Carbohydrate	49 g
Fat	2 g
Fibre	3 g
Salt	1 g

18. Which of these shapes is irregular?

   Answer: _____

   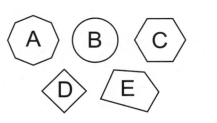

   / 7

   Carry on to the next question → →

19. What number is the arrow pointing to on the number line?

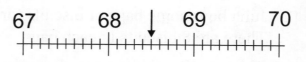

A 69.5   D 68.2

B 67.5   E 68.9

C 68.5

20. John bought 10 identical stamps. They cost £3.60 altogether.
    How much did each stamp cost?

Answer: _____ p

21. Which of these fractions is smallest?

A ¾   B ½   C ⅛   D ¼   E ⅜

22. This diagram shows the length and width of a school playground.

What is the perimeter of the playground?

Answer: _____ m

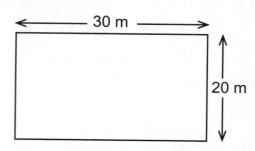

23. Jay receives £2.40 pocket money every week.

How many weeks will it take him to save £7.20?

Answer: _____ weeks

24. Tara thinks of a shape. It has 5 faces and 9 edges.
    Which of the following could be Tara's shape?

A   B   C   D   E

/ 6

Carry on to the next question →→

25. $7 + 7 + 7 + 7 = \boxed{} \times 2$

What is the missing number?

A 7   **B** 14   **C** 28   **D** 11   **E** 17

26. Siti goes cycling at 1.30 pm. She spends 35 minutes cycling and then takes a 15 minute break.

What time does her break finish?

A   2:10 pm   **C**   2:15 am   **E**   2:20 am

B   2:15 pm   **D**   2:20 pm

27. Claire has 80 stickers. She gives ½ of them to Luke. Luke then gives ¼ of his stickers to Jenny.

How many stickers does Jenny get?

A   40   **B**   30   **C**   20   **D**   10   **E**   5

28. Jemma makes a chart which shows the hair colour of the children in her class.

Which of these sentences is not true?

Colour	Number of children
Brown	14
Black	6
Blonde	7
Red	1

A   6 children have black hair.
B   Brown is the most common hair colour.
C   There are 28 children in Jemma's class.
D   8 more children have brown hair than have blonde hair.
E   15 children have brown or red hair.

29. Suki has a 2 m roll of ribbon. She cuts off 2 pieces of ribbon each measuring 75 cm.

How much ribbon is left on the roll?

A   1.25 m   **B**   0.75 m   **C**   50 m   **D**   5 m   **E**   0.5 m

30. Ruth thinks of a number. She multiplies it by 7 and then she adds 1. She ends up with 50.

What number did she start with?

A   5   **C**   6   **E**   9

B   8   **D**   7

/ 6

Assessment Test 2

Allow 35 minutes to do this test. Work as quickly and as carefully as you can.

You can print **multiple-choice answer sheets** for these questions from our website — go to www.cgplearning.co.uk/11+. If you'd prefer to answer them in standard write-in format, either write your answers in the spaces provided or circle the **correct answer** from the options **A** to **E**.

1. What is the value of the 7 in 7052?

    A   seven tenths   **C**   seven hundred   **E**   seventy
    B   seventy thousand   **D**   seven thousand

2. How many edges does a cube have?

    A   12   **B**   6   **C**   7   **D**   8   **E**   9

3. Which of the following numbers divides exactly by 8?

    A   12   **B**   63   **C**   72   **D**   84   **E**   94

4. Ahmed asked the children in his class to name their favourite type of dog. He put the results in this bar chart.

    How many children chose the most popular type of dog?

    A   9   **C**   11   **E**   37
    B   10   **D**   12

    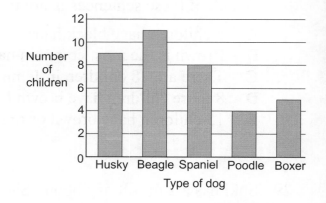

5. Look at these numbers.

    | 0.35 | 1.03 | 1.30 | 0.98 | 0.65 |

    Which of the following options shows the numbers in order from smallest to largest?

    A   0.35   0.98   0.65   1.30   1.03
    B   0.35   0.65   0.98   1.03   1.30
    C   1.30   1.03   0.98   0.65   0.35
    D   0.35   0.65   0.98   1.30   1.03
    E   1.03   1.30   0.98   0.65   0.35

    / 5

Carry on to the next question → →

6. Which of these triangles is an equilateral triangle?

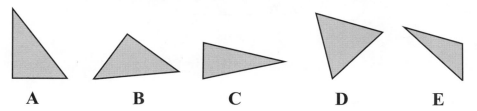

   A   **B**   **C**   **D**   **E**

7. Max is facing north. He turns to face south.

   How many right angles has he turned through?

   Answer: _____

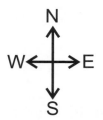

8. Which of these shapes has a line of symmetry?

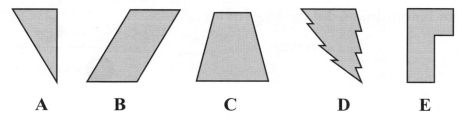

   A   **B**   **C**   **D**   **E**

9. Sarah visits her grandma every Sunday.
   She visits on 12th February.

   What is the date of the next Sunday she will visit her grandma?

   A 5th February   **C** 17th February   **E** 19th February
   B 12th March   **D** 20th February

10. [ ] < 4652

    Which of the following numbers could go in the box above?

    A 4731   **B** 4599   **C** 5120   **D** 4655   **E** 6021

11. John records the maximum temperature in Aberdeen each day for a week. He draws this bar chart to show his results.

    What is the difference between the temperature on Wednesday and on Saturday?

    Answer: _____°C

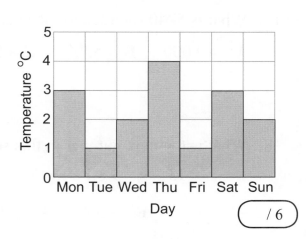

/ 6

Carry on to the next question → →

12. $\boxed{60 - 37 = 23}$

What is $560 - 237$?   Answer: _____

13. What is $4500 \div 100$?

A   400.5   **B**   0.45   **C**   4.5   **D**   45   **E**   450

14. Class 4C counted the vehicles that passed
by the window during their maths lesson.
They put the results on this pictogram.

How many buses and motorbikes did they see in total?

Answer: _____

Lorry	
Car	
Motorbike	
Bus	

⊚ = 4 vehicles

15. Apples come in packs of 6.
Ted's class need to buy enough packs so that each child can have one apple.
There are 32 children in the class.

How many packs of apples will they need?

A   5   **B**   6   **C**   8   **D**   4   **E**   7

16. £87 is shared equally between three people.

How much money do they each receive?

Answer: £ _____

17. What is 5240 rounded to the nearest hundred?

A   10 000   **B**   5300   **C**   5270   **D**   5200   **E**   5000

18. What is the next number in this sequence?

13   9   5   1   –3   ?

A   –1   **B**   –5   **C**   –6   **D**   –7   **E**   1

$\boxed{/7}$

Carry on to the next question →→

19. ¾ of the grid on the right is shaded.
    Which of the fractions below is equal to ¾?

    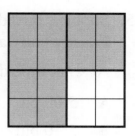

    A ¹⁴⁄₁₆ **B** ¹⁰⁄₁₆ **C** ¹²⁄₁₆ **D** ⁷⁄₁₆ **E** ⁴⁄₁₆

20. Which corner of the pentagon is at point (1, 4)?

    Answer: _____

    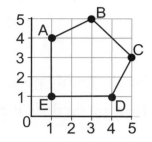

21. How many grams are there in 2½ kilograms?

    A 250 g **B** 25 g **C** 2500 g **D** 2050 g **E** 2.5 g

22. This is a diagram of Azra's trampoline.
    It is a regular hexagon.

    What is the perimeter of the trampoline?

    Answer: _____ m

23. Tom is making a pattern of squares using counters.

    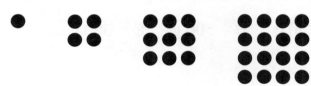

    How many counters will he need to make the next square in the pattern?

    A 20 **B** 25 **C** 30 **D** 35 **E** 36

24. Vikram's dog weighs 16 kg.
    He uses this table to work out how many
    biscuits to feed his dog each day.

    How many biscuits should Vikram
    give his dog in a week?

    A 14 **C** 15 **E** 28
    B 7   **D** 29

Dog weight	Number of biscuits a day
Up to 7 kg	1
Up to 15 kg	2
Up to 30 kg	4

/ 6

25. Sophie's birthday party starts at 4 pm and finishes at 6:30 pm.
Exactly halfway through the party the children have the birthday cake.

At what time do they have the cake?

A   5:00 pm   C   5:15 pm   E   6:00 pm

B   5:30 pm   D   5:45 pm

26. Noel's family go to the cinema.

How much does it cost for 3 children and 2 adults?

Answer: £ _____

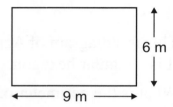

Cinema tickets
Child £3.50
Adult £7.50

27. This is a diagram of Adam's vegetable garden.

What is its area?

A   54 m²   C   15 m²   E   56 m²

B   81 m²   D   30 m²

6 m

9 m

28. A packet of raisins weighs 65 g.

What do 6 packets of raisins weigh to the nearest 100 g?

A   300 g   B   400 g   C   200 g   D   500 g   E   390 g

29. A horse has 250 ml of medicine every day.
There are 2 litres of medicine in the bottle.

How many days will the bottle of medicine last for?

Answer: _____ days

2 litres

250 ml

30. A stall sells hot dogs for £1.25 each.
Dee buys 3 hot dogs and pays with a £10 note.

How much change does she get?

A   £5.25   B   £7.52   C   £6.25   D   £7.25   E   £6.50

/ 6

Assessment Test 3

Allow 35 minutes to do this test. Work as quickly and as carefully as you can.

You can print **multiple-choice answer sheets** for these questions from our website — go to www.cgplearning.co.uk/11+. If you'd prefer to answer them in standard write-in format, either write your answers in the spaces provided or circle the **correct answer** from the options **A** to **E**.

1. What type of shape is this?

A	hexagon	**C**	octagon	**E**	triangle
B	pentagon	**D**	square		

2. Write the number three thousand and seventeen in figures.   Answer: _____

3. Omar's class are split into teams of 5 children. There are 30 children in the class. How many teams are there?

    A 8   **B** 6   **C** 4   **D** 7   **E** 5

4. Find the difference between 59 and 73.   Answer: _____

5. Class 4 made this pictogram to show the animals they saw on their country walk.

    How many sheep did they see?

    Answer: _____

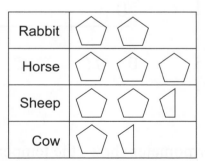

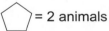

6. How many lines of symmetry does this equilateral triangle have?

    A 3   **B** 4   **C** 2   **D** 6   **E** 1

/ 6

Carry on to the next question → →

7. Edward draws this bar chart to show the favourite sports of children in his year group.

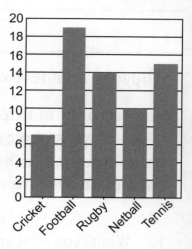

Which sport did fewest children choose?

Answer: _____

8. Which of the following pairs of numbers are both multiples of 9?

   A   90 and 72   **D**   62 and 15

   B   27 and 42   **E**   56 and 18

   C   14 and 36

9. What fraction of the hexagon is shaded?

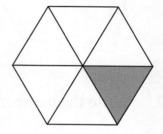

   A ⅙   **B** ⅕   **C** ⅚   **D** ⅐   **E** ¼

10. Angle y is smaller than a right angle.

    Which of the following could be the size of angle y?

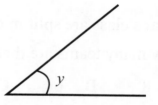

    A   120°   **C**   170°   **E**   180°

    B   40°   **D**   90°

11. What number is the arrow pointing to on this number line?

    A   0.25   **B**   0.5   **C**   7.5   **D**   0.75   **E**   0.33

12. The thermometer shows the temperature on a hilltop.
    The temperature is 3 °C warmer at the bottom of the hill.

    What is the temperature at the bottom of the hill?

    Answer: _____ °C

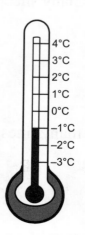

/ 6

Carry on to the next question → →

13. How many pence are there in £2.35?

Answer: _____ p

14. The diagram shows part of a map of a zoo.

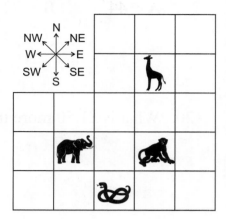

Aki is visiting the giraffes.
In which direction must he walk to reach the elephants?

A   south-west   **C**   east   **E**   south-east
B   west   **D**   south

15. Which one of the following times is the same as twenty minutes to three?

A   2:40   **B**   2:50   **C**   3:45   **D**   3:40   **E**   3:20

16. This is a diagram of a school stage.

What is its perimeter?

Answer: _____ m

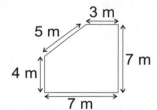

17. The diagram shows a square-based pyramid.

How many faces does it have?

Answer: _____

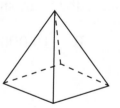

18. Look at this bus timetable.
Denise catches the bus in Shipford. She gets off at Uptown.

How long is her bus journey?

Answer: _____ minutes

Bus stop	Time
Markham	8:20 am
Shipford	8:28 am
Uptown	8:46 am

/ 6

Carry on to the next question → →

19. Katy thinks of a number. She multiplies it by 4 and gets 88.

What number was Katy thinking of?

A 44   **B** 92   **C** 84   **D** 22   **E** 352

20. What is £1.50 more than £36.90?   Answer: £ _____

21. Saroo started with the number 3 and used the rule "add 4"
to make a sequence. What is the 5th number in her sequence?

A 7   **C** 17   **E** 20

B 15   **D** 19

22. What is 37×4?   Answer: _____

23. Fiona is making ice cubes for a party.
She uses 10 ml of water to make one ice cube.

How many ice cubes can she make from one litre of water?

A 1000   **B** 10 000   **C** 10   **D** 1   **E** 100

24. Mr Tran is making a path through his vegetable
patch using hexagonal stones.

Before lunch he lays a third of the stones.
The diagram shows the path so far.

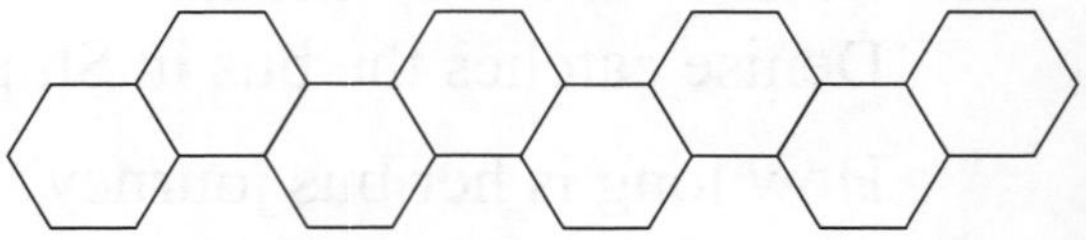

How many stones will be in the finished path?

Answer: _____

/ 6

Carry on to the next question →→

25. Freya buys a glass of juice and a cookie.

   How much change does she get from £5.00?

   A £3.19   **C** £2.91   **E** £2.19

   B £3.91   **D** £2.10

26. Which of these numbers does not equal 480 when it is rounded to the nearest 10?

   A 485   **B** 475   **C** 480.5   **D** 478   **E** 484.5

27. Look at the rectangles on the right.

   Which two rectangles have the same area?

   Answer: _____ and _____

   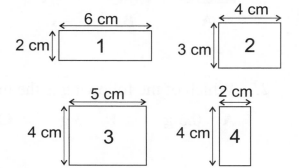

28. The ingredients for a salad for 4 people are shown on the right.
   Mika wants to make it for 12 people.

   How much olive oil should she use?

   130 g lettuce
   3 tomatoes
   45 ml olive oil
   juice of 1 lemon

   A 45 ml   **C** 90 ml   **E** 135 ml

   B 15 ml   **D** 450 ml

29. What are the coordinates of the point marked A?

   Answer: (_____ , _____)

   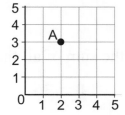

30. Henry is measuring the width of the school tennis court using his stride.
   His stride measures 80 centimetres. The court is 9 strides wide.

   What is the width of the court to the nearest metre?

   A 7 m   **B** 9 m   **C** 72 m   **D** 6 m   **E** 8 m

   / 6

Assessment Test 4

Allow 35 minutes to do this test. Work as quickly and as carefully as you can.

You can print **multiple-choice answer sheets** for these questions from our website — go to www.cgplearning.co.uk/11+. If you'd prefer to answer them in standard write-in format, either write your answers in the spaces provided or circle the **correct answer** from the options **A** to **E**.

1. Which of these shapes is a hexagon?

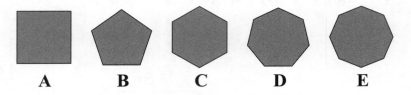

    A   **B**   **C**   **D**   **E**

2. Which of the following is the most likely weight of an apple?

    A 0.3 g   **B** 3 g   **C** 0.3 kg   **D** 3 kg   **E** 30 kg

3. Which of these numbers is the smallest?

    4.70   40.7   0.47   7.4   70.4

    Answer: _____

4. Look at this list of numbers.

    18   30   15   12   36

    Which of the following numbers is a factor of all the numbers in the list?

    A 2   **B** 3   **C** 4   **D** 5   **E** 6

5. What is the sum of all the even numbers between 1 and 9?

    A 20   **B** 36   **C** 45   **D** 16   **E** 50

6. Which of these shapes has only one line of symmetry?

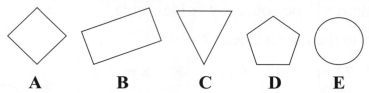

    A   **B**   **C**   **D**   **E**

/ 6

Carry on to the next question → →

7. This pictogram shows the numbers of sweets sold by a shop in one day.

Sweet	Number sold
Chocolate mice	🍬 🍬 🍬 🍬
Sherbert discs	🍬 🍬
Lollipops	🍬 🍬 🍬 🍬 🍬
Foam bananas	🍬 🍬 🍬 🍬
Strawberry laces	🍬 🍬 🍬

🍬 = 6 sweets

How many strawberry laces were sold?

Answer: _____

8. What is ¼ of 32?

Answer: _____

9. There are 24 children in a class.
Every child in the class needs one of each type of book shown in the bar chart.

Which books are there not enough of?

A Maths and Art
B Music only
C History and Music
D History and English
E Music, History and English

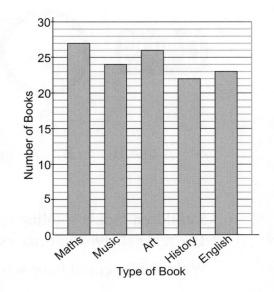

10. How many centimetres are there in 17.04 metres?

A 170 400 cm   D 170.4 cm
B 170 40 cm   E 170.04 cm
C 1704 cm

11. The temperature in Norway is -5 °C.
The temperature in Dubai is 26 °C.

What is the difference between these two temperatures?

Answer: _____ °C

12. A teacher wants to split 56 children into teams of 6.

How many complete teams can he make?

Answer: _____

/ 6

Carry on to the next question → →

Assessment Test 4

13. Which of these numbers should go in the area labelled X on this Venn diagram?

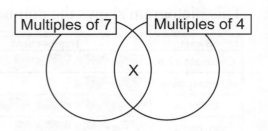

    A 14   **D** 35

    B 21   **E** 43

    C 28

14. What number is the arrow pointing to on this number line?

    Answer: _____

15. Which two clocks show the same time?

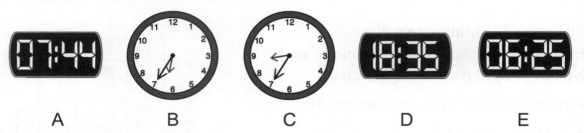

    A A and B   **B** A and D   **C** A and C   **D** B and D   **E** B and E

16. 5 children took a spelling test.
The table shows their marks rounded to the nearest 10.

    Which child could have scored 74 in the test?

Name	Rounded Mark
Paul	80
Kirsty	50
Leon	100
Hemish	70
Fiona	60

    A Paul   **D** Hemish

    B Kirsty   **E** Fiona

    C Leon

17. Which two of these diagrams have the same fraction shaded?

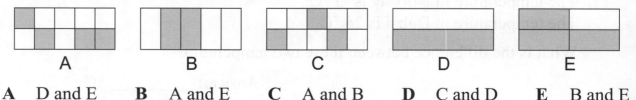

    A D and E   **B** A and E   **C** A and B   **D** C and D   **E** B and E

18. Which of these numbers is closest to 5000?

    A 4892   **B** 5029   **C** 4972   **D** 5100   **E** 4962

Carry on to the next question → →

19. Estimate the size of angle *a* in this shape.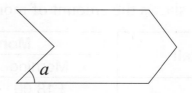

    A 90°   **D** 45°
    B 100°   **E** 180°
    C 120°

20. What is the total cost of 7 pens sold at 99p each?

    Answer: £ _____

21. Ranji buys a loaf of bread and three cans of cola.
    He pays a total of £3.00. The shop charges 90p for a loaf of bread.

    How much does one can of cola cost?

    Answer: _____ p

22. What is the missing digit in this calculation?

    $1\ \boxed{}\ \times 8 = 120$

    A 4   **B** 5   **C** 6   **D** 7   **E** 8

23. This is a net for a 3D shape. What shape will
    it make if it is folded along the dashed lines?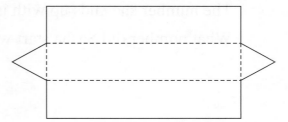

    A A cuboid
    B A triangular prism
    C A square-based pyramid
    D A polygon
    E A quadrilateral

24. A rectangle is split in half into two triangles.

    What type of triangle must each of these triangles be?

    A Scalene triangles   **D** Isosceles triangles
    B Right-angled triangles   **E** Quadrilateral triangles
    C Equilateral triangles

25. Lindsey writes a list of numbers.
    She starts with the number 13 and counts backwards in steps of 4.

    Which of these numbers will be on her list?

    A 8   **B** 4   **C** 0   **D** -3   **E** -8

Carry on to the next question → →

26. This table shows the amount of money collected by each stall at a fair.

Stall	Money Collected	
	Morning	Afternoon
Tombola	£18.00	£11.00
Coconut Shy	£15.00	£17.00
Penalty Shoot-out	£16.00	£22.00
Pony Ride	£21.00	£19.00
Bash the Rat	£13.00	£20.00

Which stall collected the most money over the whole day?

A Tombola   **D** Pony Ride

B Coconut Shy   **E** Bash the Rat

C Penalty Shoot-out

27. Esther buys a box of 100 ice pops for £36. She works out how much each ice pop cost her to buy and sells each ice pop for 14p more than this amount.

How much money does Esther sell each ice pop for?

Answer: _____ p

28. Sasha thinks of a number. She multiplies the number by 8, then adds 3. The number she ends up with is 51.

What number did Sasha start with?

Answer: _____

29. Sandeep measures the length of the playground with a stick. The playground is 30 stick lengths long. The stick is 55 cm long.

How long is the playground?

A 16.5 m   **B** 165 m   **C** 65 m   **D** 160 cm   **E** 1650 m

30. Points A, B and C lie on the corners of a rectangle. Point D lies on the fourth corner of the rectangle.

What are the coordinates of point D?

A (7, 5)   **D** (2, 8)

B (8, 4)   **E** (4, 8)

C (5, 7)

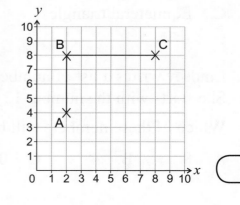

/ 5

Assessment Test 5

Allow 35 minutes to do this test. Work as quickly and as carefully as you can.

You can print **multiple-choice answer sheets** for these questions from our website — go to www.cgplearning.co.uk/11+. If you'd prefer to answer them in standard write-in format, either write your answers in the spaces provided or circle the **correct answer** from the options **A** to **E**.

1. Which number is in the wrong section of this Venn diagram?

    Answer: _____

    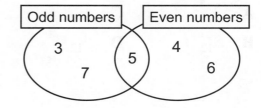

2. Mr Button is buying some tiles for his bathroom.
    He wants tiles which have 5 equal sides.

    What shape should his tiles be?

    A circle   **D** regular pentagon
    B regular hexagon   **E** square
    C triangle

3. One minibus has space for 9 passengers.

    How many minibuses are needed for 72 passengers?

    A 8   **B** 6   **C** 12   **D** 7   **E** 15

4. Chris is making flapjacks. The scales show
    the weight of the sugar that he uses.

    How much sugar does Chris use?

    Answer: _____ g

5. Which of the following is the most likely height of a house?

    A 0.85 km   **D** 85 cm
    B 850 mm   **E** 80.5 m
    C 8.5 m

/ 5

Carry on to the next question → →

6. Which pair of numbers can go in the shaded box of the table?

   A 8 and 12   D 6 and 8
   B 7 and 9   E 9 and 10
   C 3 and 6

	odd numbers	even numbers
>10	11 15	12 20
<10	3 5	

7. What fraction of this shape is shaded?

   A ³⁄₁₂   C ⁷⁄₁₂   E ⁸⁄₁₂
   B ⁵⁄₁₂   D ⁴⁄₁₂

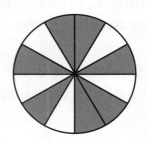

8. Which of these numbers is not a multiple of 3 and 5?

   A 15   B 30   C 35   D 60   E 45

9. Round 17.48 m to the nearest 0.1 m.

   Answer: _____ m

10. One 20p coin weighs 5 g.

    How much will 20p coins worth £1 weigh?

    A 25 g   B 125 g   C 1.25 kg   D 250 g   E 2.5 kg

11. What is 1000 – 567?

    A 437   B 441   C 563   D 433   E 537

12. The table shows the temperature in Antarctica on five days.

    What was the difference in temperature between Wednesday and Thursday?

    A 6 °C   D 4 °C
    B 7 °C   E 5 °C
    C 12 °C

Day	Temperature (°C)
Monday	-6
Tuesday	-4
Wednesday	-7
Thursday	-12
Friday	-8

/ 7

Carry on to the next question →→

13. $\boxed{} \div 8 = 70$

What is the missing number in this calculation?

Answer: _____

14.   The pictogram shows the scores of five teams in a quiz.

What is the difference between the scores of Team 2 and Team 5?

Answer: _____ points

Team 1	✦ ✦ ✦
Team 2	✦ ✦
Team 3	✦ ✦ ✦ ✦ ⟩
Team 4	✦ ◊
Team 5	✦ ✦ ✦ ⟩

✦ = 6 points

15.   A train leaves Birmingham at 8:57 and arrives in Manchester at 10:45.

How long did the journey take?

A   2 hours and 48 minutes   **D**   1 hour and 48 minutes

B   1 hour and 45 minutes   **E**   1 hour and 42 minutes

C   2 hours and 12 minutes

16.   Aaron is laying concrete blocks to make a path.
Each block weighs 3 kg.

How much would three blocks weigh in grams?

A   90 g   **B**   9000 g   **C**   9.9 g   **D**   900 g   **E**   3000 g

17.   Cameron is following a path on this coordinate grid. He starts at B7 and goes 5 squares south and 3 squares east.

What are the coordinates of the square that he reaches?

Answer: _____

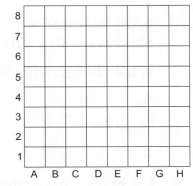

18.   Here is part of a sequence:

...12, 24, 48, 96...

The rule for the sequence is 'double the previous number'.

Which number came before 12 in the sequence?

Answer: _____

/ 6

Carry on to the next question → →

Assessment Test 5

19. Akmal folds up a net to make a cube.

    Which of the following nets could he have used?

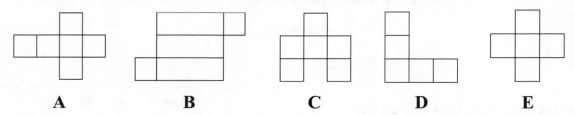

    A   **B**   **C**   **D**   **E**

20. Shape X is reflected in a vertical mirror line.

    Which of the following shapes is the reflection of shape X?

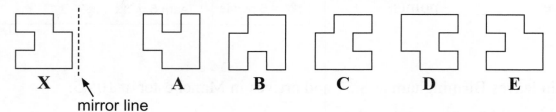

    X   **A**   **B**   **C**   **D**   **E**

    mirror line

21. Kirsten's bookshelf is 1 m long.
    She has some books which are all 7 cm thick.

    How many books can she fit on her bookshelf?

    A 7   **B** 15   **C** 13   **D** 14   **E** 16

22. The bar chart shows the height of six buildings.

    What is the difference in height between building 3
    and building 5?

                    Answer: _____ m

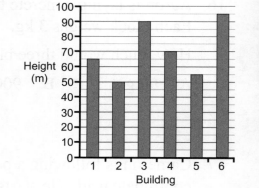

23. Kaya buys 4 oranges at 49p each.
    She pays with a £10 note.

    What change will she be given?

    A £1.96   **C** £7.62   **E** £4.90
    B £8.04   **D** £9.02

24. Liz makes this shape using six white cubes.
    She paints the outside of the shape blue and
    then breaks the shape apart into cubes again.

    How many cube faces are white?

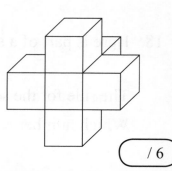

    A 10   **B** 12   **C** 8   **D** 5   **E** 7

    / 6

Carry on to the next question → →

25. A jug contains 3 litres of water. Maxine pours
    six 200 ml glasses of water from the jug.

    How much water is left in the jug?

    A   1200 ml   C   600 ml   E   1500 ml
    B   1800 ml   D   2400 ml

26. Which of these statements is true?
    A   A cube has four faces.
    B   A triangle-based pyramid has one rectangular face.
    C   A square-based pyramid has four triangular faces.
    D   A cylinder has no curved faces.
    E   A triangular prism has three triangular faces.

27. Each chapter in a book is eight pages long.
    Susi reads the first 8 chapters and 5 pages of chapter 9.

    How many pages has Susi read?   Answer: _____ pages

28. Alia's cat eats 85 g of tinned meat a day.

    How much tinned meat does her cat eat in a week?

    A   705 g   B   560 g   C   635 g   D   595 g   E   460 g

29. The battery of Darren's mobile phone lasts for 50 hours
    before he has to charge it again. The battery is fully
    charged at 9 am on Sunday morning.

    When will Darren have to charge the battery again?

    A   1 pm Tuesday   D   11 am Tuesday
    B   11 pm Monday   E   5 am Wednesday
    C   11 am Wednesday

30. Harvey draws points A and B on this coordinate grid.
    He draws point C and then draws a line between points
    B and C to make a right angle.

    Which of the following could be the coordinates of point C?

    A   (2, 4)   C   (2, 1)   E   (5, 4)
    B   (3, 2)   D   (3, 3)

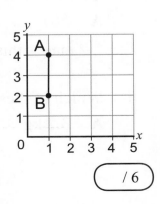

/ 6

Assessment Test 5

Assessment Test 6

Allow 35 minutes to do this test. Work as quickly and as carefully as you can.

You can print **multiple-choice answer sheets** for these questions from our website — go to www.cgplearning.co.uk/11+. If you'd prefer to answer them in standard write-in format, either write your answers in the spaces provided or circle the **correct answer** from the options **A** to **E**.

1. Which of these numbers is the largest?

    113   134   3.4   13   34

    Answer: _____

2. The bar chart shows the amount of rain on an island during the first six months of a year.

    Which month had the highest amount of rain?

    Answer: _____

    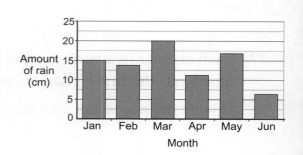

3. What number is 110 less than 1000?

    A 880   **B** 910   **C** 990   **D** 890   **E** 900

4. Mick adds up the 7 digits on this barcode.

    What answer does he get?

    Answer: _____

    0 5 1 5 6 4 7

5. There are 606 chickens at Raven Farm.
    There are 149 fewer chickens at Shrove Farm.

    How many chickens are there at Shrove Farm?

    A 567   **B** 457   **C** 543   **D** 467   **E** 563

6. Which of these weights is closest to 3 kg?

    A 3.2 kg   **B** 2.8 kg   **C** 2.9 kg   **D** 2.5 kg   **E** 3.3 kg

/ 6

Carry on to the next question →→

7. The pictogram shows the number of hours of sunshine on five days.

How many more hours of sunshine were there on Thursday than on Monday?

Answer: _____ hours

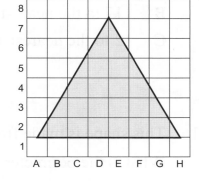

Monday	☀ ◗
Tuesday	☀
Wednesday	☀ ☀ ☀
Thursday	☀ ☀
Friday	☀

☀ = 4 hours

8. Which pair of numbers have a difference of 13?

A 61 and 55   **C** 44 and 56   **E** 34 and 48

B 77 and 91   **D** 58 and 71

9. Olivia draws this triangle on a coordinate grid.

Which of these squares is not inside the triangle?

A C3   **C** E5   **E** F7

B D5   **D** D2

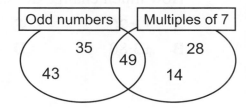

10. Taj starts at 17 and counts back in steps of 5.

Which of these numbers will be in his sequence?

A 1   **B** 2   **C** 3   **D** 4   **E** 5

11. Which number is in the wrong section of this Venn diagram?

Answer: _____

Odd numbers   Multiples of 7

35   28
   49
43   14

12. A TV programme starts at 17:45 and lasts for 57 minutes.

What time does the programme finish?

A 18:48   **B** 6:43   **C** 18:42   **D** 16:42   **E** 19:48

13. Anne-Marie can make 4 necklaces out of 320 beads. Each necklace has the same amount of beads.

How many beads are there in each necklace?

A 90   **C** 80   **E** 140

B 160   **D** 100

/ 7

Carry on to the next question →→

Assessment Test 6

14. Priya draws this shape on some squared paper.
Each square on the paper has an area of 1 cm².

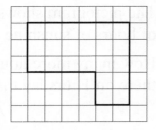

What is the area of Priya's shape?

   A   22 cm²   **C**   15 cm²   **E**   18 cm²
   B   10 cm²   **D**   24 cm²

15. Which of these is equal to 120?

   A   121 to the nearest 100   **D**   119.4 to the nearest whole number
   B   117 to the nearest 10   **E**   125 to the nearest 10
   C   12 to the nearest 100

16. This shape is made from five identical rectangles.

What is the perimeter of the shape?

                    Answer: _____ cm

17. A postcard costs 40p. Nikki buys three postcards.

How much change does she receive from £5?

   A   £1.20   **C**   £4.60   **E**   £4.20
   B   £3.80   **D**   £4.00

18. What is 90 × 9?

   A   999   **C**   900   **E**   810
   B   891   **D**   890

19. Which pair of values are equal?

   A   0.1 and ¼   **C**   ¾ and 0.25   **E**   ½ and 0.5
   B   ³⁄₁₀ and 0.4   **D**   ⁷⁄₁₀ and 0.5

/ 6

Carry on to the next question → →

20. A car uses 2 litres of fuel to travel 12 miles.

How many litres of fuel will the car need to travel 72 miles?

Answer: _____ litres

21. Brian made this bar chart to record how much his plant grew each week.

How much did the plant grow in total during weeks 4, 5 and 6?

Answer: _____ cm

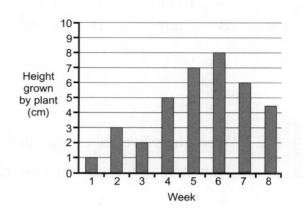

22. Ada bought a bag containing 15 marbles. She gave $\frac{1}{5}$ of the marbles to Jenni.

How many marbles did Ada have left?

A 12   **B** 3   **C** 10   **D** 5   **E** 9

23. Chelsea reflected this rectangle in the mirror line.

Which point shows the reflection of point Z?

A   **B**   **C**   **D**   **E**

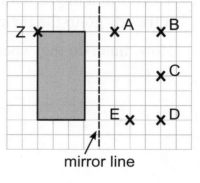

24. Look at the two jugs of orange juice shown on the right.

How much orange juice is there in total?

A 2500 ml   **C** 3050 ml   **E** 2650 ml
B 2150 ml   **D** 3500 ml

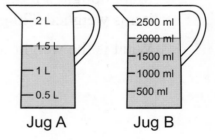

25. Which of these nets will fold up to make a square-based pyramid?

        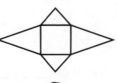

A   **B**   **C**   **D**   **E**

/ 6

Carry on to the next question → →

Assessment Test 6

26. A shop keeps ice cream in a freezer at -16 °C.
    The freezer breaks down at 4 am and the temperature
    in the freezer rises by 1 °C every hour.

    At what time will the temperature in the freezer reach -9 °C?

    A   10 am   **C**   1 pm   **E**   9 am
    B   7 am   **D**   11 am

27. Wen glues five cubes together to make this shape.

    How many faces do not have glue on them?

    A   22   **C**   16   **E**   24
    B   20   **D**   17

    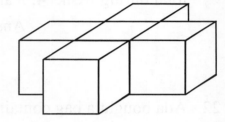

28. Tickets to a theme park cost £9.50.
    8 friends go to the theme park.

    How much do they spend on their tickets in total?

    Answer: £ _____

29. Mara bought a block of cheese and two packs of butter. The three
    items weighed 920 g in total. The block of cheese weighed 470 g.

    What is the weight of one pack of butter?

    Answer: _____ g

30. Mr Green started filling in this table to record
    the number of children from Years 4 and 5
    who were going on a school trip.

    How many Year 4 girls went on the trip?

    Answer: _____

	Year 4	Year 5	Total
Boys	22	9	31
Girls	?		28
Total		26	59

/ 5

Assessment Test 6